CHANGES

Written and Illustrated
by Penny Condon

Canadian Cataloguing in Publication Data

Condon, Penny, 1968-

Changes

ISBN 0-920915-43-4

1. Métis --Juvenile fiction. I. Gabriel Dumont Institute of Native Studies and Applied Research. II. Title

PS8555.05196 C46 2000   jC813' .5   C00-920121-1
PZ7.C7588 Cha 2000

© 2000
Gabriel Dumont Institute
505-23rd Street East
Saskatoon, Saskatchewan S7K 4K7
(306) 249-9400
www.gdins.org

Printed in Canada

Dedication

For my daughter Sydney who enjoys every season

and to Laurel for her input and guidance on this book.

Kona liked to laugh out loud, but once
she started she could not stop.

(Kona means snow in Cree)

So Kona decided to ask the Gathering Spirit how to stop from feeling so happy.

The spirit said, "Kona, you have to think of something that is going to make you feel sad."

As Kona walked home she started to think of all the trees and how the leaves were beautiful colours of red, yellow and green. She knew that soon the trees would be bare.

Kona became sad and could not stop feeling this way so...

She asked the Gathering Spirit how to stop feeling sad.

The spirit said, "Kona, you have to think of something that is going to make you feel angry!"

As Kona walked home she started to think about all the leaves on the ground and how the snow would soon cover the beautiful colours.

Kona became angry
and could not stop
feeling this way so...

She asked the Gathering Spirit how to
stop feeling angry.

The spirit said, "Kona, you
have to think of something that
is going to make you feel
surprised!"

As Kona walked home she started to think about the snow melting, and how everything on the earth begins to grow. She thought about the animals that come out to play, and she became surprised by this miracle.

Kona went one last time to the Gathering Spirit and asked, "Why did you want me to think of things that made me feel sad, angry and surprised?"

The Gathering Spirit said, "Kona, you have experienced feelings that have helped you see that our emotions change like the seasons. You have learned that one season cannot exist without the other."

The spirit smiled and said,
"How do you feel now?"

Kona replied, "I feel loved. Thank you Gathering Spirit for your beautiful teachings."